A Day in Code:
PYTHON

Learn to code in Python through an illustrated story

By Shari Eskenas

Illustrated by Ana Quintero Villafraz

Published by Sundae Electronics LLC
https://www.sundaelectronics.com

First edition 2021.

ISBN 978-1-73590-793-2 (Hardcover)
ISBN 978-1-73590-794-9 (Paperback)
ISBN 978-1-73590-795-6 (eBook)

Day turns into night and night turns into day...

The world is filled with logic. -S.E.

Once upon a time, there lived a brother and sister who loved listening to their computers tell stories to them.

Stories of fantasy and adventure were spoken through the computers' speakers. The kids enjoyed relaxing and gazing at the illustrations on the screens.

One day, the kids decided to have an adventurous day of their own. Instead of listening to the computers' stories, they wanted to tell their own story to the computers.

The kids soon realized that the computers couldn't understand them! Computers read and understand information in their own language- a computer programming language!

They needed to write **code** to communicate their story to the computers. Code is a set of instructions written for a computer to perform tasks (such as printing words on the screen). Similarly, a recipe like the one below is a set of instructions used to perform the task of making chocolate chip cookies!

A **program** is a collection of code that can be run by a computer. The kids needed to choose a programming language to write the programs in. They found that different programming languages are written in different ways and designed for different uses. As they were deciding what programming language to write their programs in, they went to a bakery and bought cupcakes.

When they got home and opened the box, they saw the cupcakes were arranged in a pattern that resembled a snake! This made them think of the **Python programming language,** so they decided to tell the story of their epic day to the computers using Python programs.

The kids learned that there are rules for writing the code, called the **syntax**. For example, in the Python language, a hash symbol (#) must be placed at the beginning of a line of code to indicate a **comment**. A comment is a note written for a person reading the code and is ignored by the computer.

To remember this, the kids drew hash symbols all around the house.

After the kids learned more about the Python language, they both wrote one line of code on their computers. After pressing the Enter key on the computer's keyboard, a **statement** (a complete program instruction) had been written.

This is their first Python program and what they learned:

```python
# The day before our epic day
feeling = 'excited'
print("We can't wait for tomorrow!")
```

Lines of code are separated with empty lines just to make the code easier to read. The program's statements are executed from top to bottom.

`# The day before our epic day` is called a **comment**, which is indicated by the hash symbol (#) in front of the line. It is written as a note for someone reading the code and is ignored by the computer. A comment can explain the purpose of the code or how it works.

`'excited'` is a **string**, which is a sequence of characters (letters, numbers, symbols, or spaces). A string can be written within two single (') or two double (") quotation marks.

`feeling` is a **variable**, which stores a value. A variable is given a name and created once a value is assigned to it. You assign a value to a variable with an equal sign (=), which is called an **assignment operator**. **Operators** are special symbols that perform operations on values or variables. In this program, `'excited'` is the value assigned to the `feeling` variable. Variable names are conventionally written in lowercase letters and an underscore (_) separates words in the name because variable names cannot contain blank spaces. They can contain letters, numbers, and underscores. A variable name cannot start with a number.

`print()` is a **function** that is built into the Python language. A function is a block of code that contains instructions to perform a specific task. The code block is run (executed) when the function is called with its name followed by parentheses. The `print()` function prints the text passed to it within the parentheses to the standard output device (computer screen).

The string `"We can't wait for tomorrow!"` is passed to the `print()` function. Therefore, when the program is run (executed), `We can't wait for tomorrow!` is printed on the computer screen.

The kids spent more time studying the Python language and were soon ready to tell their story using Python code. You'll now see the programs they gave to their computers. At the end of the book, there are directions for running the programs on YOUR computer! I hope you enjoy the story as much as the computers did!

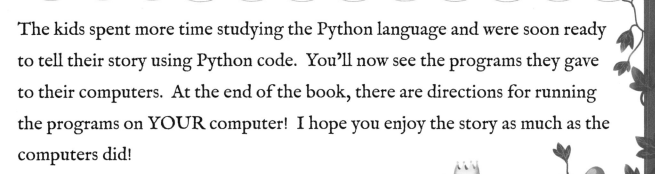

WE WERE SO EXCITED FOR TOMORROW, WE COULDN'T SLEEP. AT MIDNIGHT, WE EACH COUNTED 4 DRAGONS BEFORE FINALLY FALLING ASLEEP.

```python
# Fall asleep program

dragons = 0

for dragon_count in range(1,5):
    dragons = dragons + 1

print("I counted " + str(dragons) + " dragons and fell asleep.")
```

The variable dragons is assigned (or initialized to) a value of 0:
Since it is not within single or double quotation marks, 0 is stored in dragons as a **number**. Since 0 is an integer (a number that doesn't have a decimal point), dragons holds a value with an **integer data type**. A variable's data type determines how it can be used. For example, a number can be added to an integer but not to a string.

A code block is indicated by indented lines:
This for loop has a code block containing one line of code, which is the indented line dragons = dragons + 1. By convention, four spaces are used for the indentation in a code block. However, you can indent the lines of code by a different amount if you indent all the lines in the code block by the same amount.

The built-in Python function range() creates a sequence of integer numbers:
In this program, the range start value is 1 and the stop value is 5, which creates values from 1 through 4 because the stop value is not included.

A for loop is used to loop through a code block for a specific number of times:
A for loop is created with the Python **keywords** for and in. Keywords are reserved words that have special meanings in Python, so they cannot be used as variable or function names.

The for loop's code block is executed each time the loop is repeated (iterated). The loop repeats for each value from 1 through 4 that is created from the range() function. Therefore, the for loop repeats four times. For each iteration of the loop, the current number generated by range() is stored in the variable dragon_count. This variable can be any name-dragon_count was chosen because it's a meaningful name. A colon (:) is required at the end of the first for loop line.

The line dragons = dragons + 1 increases the dragons value by 1. The equal sign (=) is an **assignment operator** that assigns the value on the right side of the operator to the variable on the left side. Since the loop repeats four times, dragons holds a value of 4 once the loop is done.

Multiple strings can be combined with a plus sign (+), which is called concatenation:
A string can only be concatenated (combined) with other strings. Therefore, dragons must be converted from an integer into a string to be combined with strings in print(). The built-in function str() converts the value in its parentheses into a string. The plus sign (+) before and after str(dragons) combines (concatenates) the dragons value (4) that has been converted into a string with the strings "I counted " and " dragons and fell asleep.". Notice that there is a space after counted and before dragons so that there's a space before and after 4 in the complete sentence printed by print(), which is I counted 4 dragons and fell asleep.

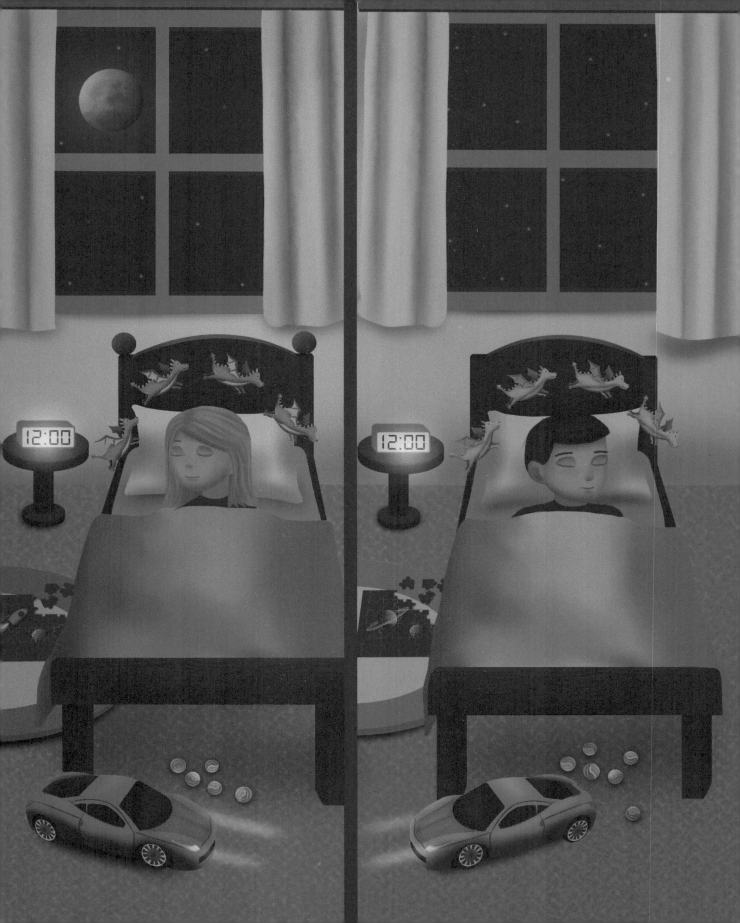

IF THE TIME IS 9 AM, THE ALARM WILL TURN ON AND WE'LL WAKE UP. IF IT'S NOT 9 AM, THE ALARM WILL BE OFF AND WE'LL BE SLEEPING. IT'S 9 AM, SO THE ALARM TURNED ON. WE'RE WAKING UP AND STRETCHING! IT'S A BEAUTIFUL DAY OUTSIDE!

☀ ☀ ☀ ☀ ☀ ☀ ☀ ☀ ☀ ☀ ☀ ☀ ☀ ☀ ☀ ☀ ☀ ☀ ☀ ☀

```python
# Wake up program

clock_time = 9
time_of_day = "AM"

if clock_time == 9 and time_of_day == "AM":
    alarm = "on"
    print("It's 9 AM! The alarm just turned " + alarm)
    print("Wake up and stretch!")
else:
    alarm = "off"
    print("Go back to sleep, the alarm is " + alarm)
```

☀ ☀ ☀ ☀ ☀ ☀ ☀ ☀ ☀ ☀ ☀ ☀ ☀ ☀ ☀ ☀ ☀ ☀ ☀ ☀

The variable clock_time is assigned a value of 9. The variable time_of_day is assigned a value of "AM", which has a **string data type.**

An if statement tests if a condition is true or false. Its code block executes if the condition is true:
An if statement is called a **conditional statement.** An **expression** is a piece of code that evaluates to a single value. The expression on the first line of the if statement, which must end with a colon (:), is the condition that is tested for being true or false. If the condition is true, the if statement's code block is executed, which consists of three indented lines in this program. If the condition is false, the else code block is executed instead.

A comparison (relational) operator compares the relation between two values:
In the if statement's condition, the **double equal sign (==)** is called an **equality operator,** which is a type of comparison operator. It tests if the value on the left side of the operator is equal to the value on the right side of the operator. Since clock_time holds a value of 9, the expression clock_time == 9 is true. Since time_of_day holds a value of "AM", time_of_day == "AM" is also a true expression.

and **is a logical operator that combines two conditions by testing if both conditions are true:**
If both conditions to the right and left side of the and operator are true, the overall expression is evaluated to be true. Otherwise, the overall expression is evaluated to be false.

Since both conditions clock_time == 9 and time_of_day == "AM" are true, the if code block is executed. The alarm variable is created and assigned a value of "on". The following print() function then prints It's 9 AM! The alarm just turned on and the next print() function prints Wake up and stretch! on the next line.

WE EACH MADE A BIG WAFFLE FOR BREAKFAST. WE FIRST ADDED STRAWBERRIES AND BANANA SLICES TO OUR WAFFLES BUT THEN DECIDED TO ADD ICE CREAM, CHOCOLATE SYRUP, AND POWDERED SUGAR! LET'S EAT!

```
# Breakfast program

cook_time = 5
total_time = cook_time * 2
print("We made two waffles in " + str(total_time) + " minutes.\n")

waffle_toppings = ["strawberries", "banana slices"]

print("I like " + waffle_toppings[0] + " and " + waffle_toppings[1] + ".")
print("But let's add some more toppings.\n")

favorite_topping = "ice cream"
waffle_toppings.append(favorite_topping)
waffle_toppings.append("chocolate syrup")
waffle_toppings.append("powdered sugar")

print("These are all the toppings now:")
for topping in waffle_toppings:
    print(topping.title())
```

`total_time` is assigned a value of `cook_time * 2`, which uses the **multiplication operator** (`*`) to multiply `cook_time` by 2. The `print()` function prints `We made two waffles in 10 minutes.` The newline character (`\n`) creates an empty line before the line that is printed by the next `print()`.

`waffle_toppings` **is a variable that holds a list. A list is an ordered sequence of items:**
A **list** is a Python data type. It contains **items** (also called elements) separated by commas between two brackets (`[ ]`). A list can contain items of any data type and the items can be of different data types. The `waffle_toppings` list initially contains the strings `"strawberries"` and `"banana slices"`.

Each item in a list can be accessed with an index number within brackets:
The first item in a list starts at an index (position number) of `0`. `waffle_toppings[0]` stores the first item and `waffle_toppings[1]` stores the second item in the `waffle_toppings` list. The next `print()` function prints `I like strawberries and banana slices.`

`append()` **adds an item to the end of a list. It is called a method:**
A **method** is a function that can perform an action on data. `append()` is a built-in Python method. In this program, `append()` acts on the list `waffle_toppings` to add the strings `"ice cream"`, `"chocolate syrup"`, and `"powdered sugar"` to the end of the list. The `append()` method is called (executed) using **dot notation**. A dot (`.`) is required between the variable name `waffle_toppings` and the method name `append`. Opening and closing parentheses are required after the method name. As you can see, the item within the `append()` parentheses that is passed to the method can be a variable (`favorite_topping`) or the value itself.

The `for` **loop prints each item in the** `waffle_toppings` **list that now includes the appended items:**
The `for` loop repeats for each item in the `waffle_toppings` list. For each loop iteration, the current list item is stored in `topping` and `print()` prints it. The built-in method `title()` acts on `topping` to capitalize the first letter of each topping and has empty parentheses because it doesn't need extra information.

```
# Kite flying program

print("There are four different kites available right now.\n")

kite_1 = {'shape':'diamond-shaped', 'color':'blue'}
kite_2 = {'shape':'rectangular', 'color':'green'}
kite_3 = {'shape':'triangular', 'color':'purple'}
kite_4 = {'shape':'star-shaped', 'color':'yellow'}

print("I'd like the " + kite_1['color'] + ", " + kite_1['shape'] + " kite")
print("I'd like the " + kite_3['color'] + ", " + kite_3['shape'] + " kite\n")

# Create a list of four dictionaries
kites_available = [kite_1, kite_2, kite_3, kite_4]

kites_available.remove(kite_1)
kites_available.remove(kite_3)

kites_left = len(kites_available)
print(str(kites_left) + " kites are left that have these features:")
print(kites_available)

print("\nLet's fly our kites!")
```

kite_1, kite_2, kite_3, and kite_4 are variables that hold dictionaries:
A **dictionary** is a Python data type. It is a collection of items that store related pieces of information within curly braces ({}). Each item in a dictionary consists of a **key** and its associated **value**, which are separated by a colon (:) and called a **key:value pair**. The dictionary's items are separated by commas. A dictionary's values can be of any data type. A dictionary's keys must be of a data type such as an integer or string that is **immutable**, which means the values of the keys can't change. An example of a **mutable** data type is a list because the items it contains can be updated.

In the kite_1 dictionary, the key 'shape' has a value of 'diamond-shaped' and the key 'color' has a value of 'blue'.

A key's value is accessed by including the key in brackets ([ ]) after the dictionary's name:
For example, to access the value of the 'color' key in the kite_1 dictionary, use kite_1['color']. The first print() after the dictionaries are defined prints I'd like the blue, diamond-shaped kite and the next print() prints I'd like the purple, triangular kite.

kites_available is a list containing the four dictionaries kite_1, kite_2, kite_3, and kite_4:
Each item in the kites_available list stores a dictionary. The built-in Python method remove() removes a specified item from a list. The remove() method is used to remove the list items kite_1 and kite_3 from the kites_available list. The built-in function len() returns the length (number of items) of the kites_available list. The length of 2 is stored in kites_left, which is converted into a string with the str() function in print(). The remaining dictionaries in the kites_available list (stored in the variables kite_2 and kite_4) are printed by print(kites_available). The newline character (\n) at the beginning of a string in print() adds an empty line before the string is printed.

IF THE PRETZEL BAG IS OPEN OR THE DONUT BOX IS OPEN, AND WE'RE BUILDING A SANDCASTLE, SEAGULLS WILL BE EATING. IF THE PRETZEL BAG IS OPEN OR THE DONUT BOX IS OPEN, AND WE'RE NOT BUILDING A SANDCASTLE, WE WILL BE WATCHING OUT FOR SEAGULLS. OTHERWISE, IF THE PRETZEL BAG IS NOT OPEN AND THE DONUT BOX IS NOT OPEN, SEAGULLS WILL NOT BE EATING. SINCE THE DONUT BOX IS OPEN AND WE'RE BUILDING A SANDCASTLE, SEAGULLS ARE EATING.

```
# Beach program

flags = ('red', 'blue')
print("We have " + flags[0] + " & " + flags[1] + " flags for the sandcastle.")

pretzel_bag = "closed"
donut_box = "open"
building_sandcastle = True

if pretzel_bag == "open" or donut_box == "open": # outer if statement
    if building_sandcastle: # inner if statement
        print("\nSeagulls are eating")
    else:
        print("\nWatching out for seagulls")
else:
    print("\nSeagulls are not eating")
```

`flags` **is a tuple, which is a sequence of items like a list, but the items can't be changed:**
A tuple is a Python data type. It contains a collection of items within parentheses. You cannot add or remove items from a tuple, so use it when you have a collection of items that you don't need to update. The first item has an index (position number) of 0. The `print()` function prints `We have red & blue flags for the sandcastle.`

The Boolean data type (also called the bool data type) has only two values: `True` or `False`:
The first letters of `True` and `False` must be capitalized and the rest of the letters must be lowercase. When an expression is tested for being true or false, the result will have a Boolean data type. After an `if` statement's condition is tested, it is evaluated to be a Boolean value of `True` or `False`. The variable `building_sandcastle` stores the value `True`, which is not in quotation marks because it's stored as a Boolean value rather than a string.

`or` **is a logical operator that tests if at least one condition is true:**
If the expressions to the left and right sides of the `or` operator are both true or if either expression is true, the overall expression is evaluated to be true. The condition `pretzel_bag == "open"` is false, but `donut_box == "open"` is true, so the `if` code block is executed.

An inner (nested) `if` **statement is within the code block of the outer** `if` **statement:**
The inner `if` statement tests if `building_sandcastle` is true. The `if` condition could also be written as `if building_sandcastle == True`, but this is redundant because any `if` condition evaluates to a Boolean value and does not need to be directly compared to `True`. `building_sandcastle` evaluates to a Boolean value of `True`. Therefore, the inner `if` code block is executed and `Seagulls are eating` is printed.

We're at the carnival playing the balloon darts game! If the number of balloons popped is greater than 0 and less than or equal to 2, you win a small dragon. If the number of balloons popped is greater than or equal to 3 and less than 5, you win a medium dragon. If the number of balloons popped is equal to 5, you win a large dragon. Otherwise, if you don't pop any balloons, try again. We each popped 5 balloons, so we each won a large dragon!

```
# Balloon darts program

balloons_popped = 5

if balloons_popped > 0 and balloons_popped <= 2:
    dragon_size = "small"
elif balloons_popped >= 3 and balloons_popped < 5:
    dragon_size = "medium"
elif balloons_popped == 5:
    dragon_size = "large"
else:
    dragon_size = ""
    print("Try again!")

if dragon_size:
    print("You won a " + dragon_size + " dragon!")
```

elif adds more test conditions to an if...else statement:
You can add any number of test conditions to an if...else statement with elif, which is short for "else if". If there are multiple true conditions, only the code block of the first true condition is executed.

The if...elif...else statement uses comparison operators that compare two values:
>= tests for "greater than or equal to" and <= tests for "less than or equal to". If the balloons_popped value is greater than 0 and less than or equal to 2, dragon_size is assigned a value of "small". If the balloons_popped value is greater than or equal to 3 and less than 5, dragon_size is assigned a value of "medium". If the balloons_popped value is equal to 5, dragon_size is assigned a value of "large". Otherwise, the else block is executed and dragon_size is assigned an empty string ("") and Try again! is printed. Since the variable balloons_popped stores a value of 5, the second elif expression is true and dragon_size is assigned a value of "large".

An empty string or a number with a value of zero evaluates to False:
The next if statement tests if dragon_size is a non-empty string, which will evaluate to True. The if statement won't be executed if dragon_size was assigned an empty string ("") in the else block. Since the value of dragon_size is "large", the if statement is true and print() prints You won a large dragon!

We're jumping in a bouncy castle at an amusement park!

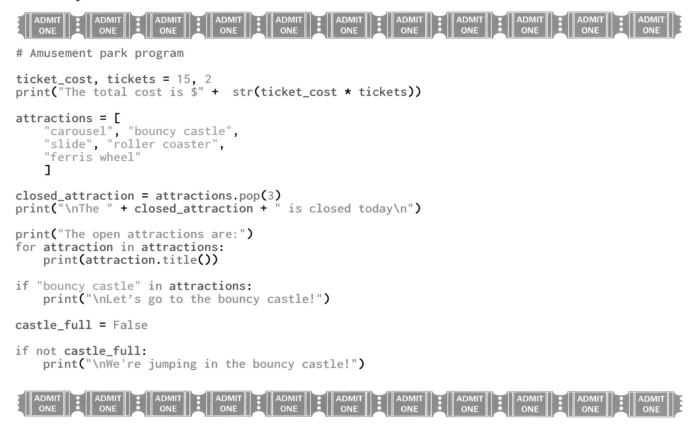

```
# Amusement park program

ticket_cost, tickets = 15, 2
print("The total cost is $" +  str(ticket_cost * tickets))

attractions = [
    "carousel", "bouncy castle",
    "slide", "roller coaster",
    "ferris wheel"
    ]

closed_attraction = attractions.pop(3)
print("\nThe " + closed_attraction + " is closed today\n")

print("The open attractions are:")
for attraction in attractions:
    print(attraction.title())

if "bouncy castle" in attractions:
    print("\nLet's go to the bouncy castle!")

castle_full = False

if not castle_full:
    print("\nWe're jumping in the bouncy castle!")
```

`ticket_cost` **is assigned a value of** `15` **and** `tickets` **is assigned a value of** `2`:
You can assign values to multiple variables on one line by separating variables with commas on the left side of the equal sign and having their corresponding values separated by commas on the right side of the equal sign. `The total cost is $30` is printed.

The `pop()` **method removes an item in a list and allows you to access the item after it's removed:**
By default, the built-in method `pop()` removes the last item in a list, but you can remove any item by including its index (position number) in parentheses. `attractions.pop(3)` removes the fourth item (because the index of the first list item starts at `0`). The removed item `"roller coaster"` is returned by the `pop()` method and stored in `closed_attraction`. The next `print()` prints `The roller coaster is closed today`. The `for` loop prints the remaining items in the `attractions` list with capitalized first letters from the `title()` method.

To define a long list over multiple lines, it's good practice to format it like the `attractions` list.

The keyword `in` **is used to test if a value is contained in a sequence such as a list:**
The `if` statement's test expression `"bouncy castle" in attractions` tests if `"bouncy castle"` is an item in the `attractions` list. Since this expression is true, `Let's go to the bouncy castle!` is printed.

`not` **is a logical operator that inverts an expression's** `True` **or** `False` **value:**
If the expression after `not` is `True`, it will be evaluated as `False`. If the expression after `not` is `False`, it will be evaluated as `True`. Since `castle_full` stores a value of `False`, the `if` condition is evaluated to be `True` and `We're jumping in the bouncy castle!` is printed.

We're ordering 2 medium cheese pizzas with one thick-crust and one crispy thin-crust pizza. We added the extra cheese and garlic toppings to the pizzas. Each pizza costs $7.99 and the cost of each topping is $0.99, so the total cost of the order is $7.99 x 2 + $0.99 x 4 = $19.94.

```python
# Pizza ordering program

# Function definitions
def pizza_type(size, crust):
    print("I would like a " + crust + "-crust, " + size + " pizza")

def calculate_cost(total_pizzas, total_toppings, pizza_cost):
    total_cost = total_pizzas * pizza_cost + total_toppings * topping_cost
    return total_cost

# These variables have a float data type since the numbers have a decimal point
small_cost, medium_cost, large_cost, topping_cost = 4.99, 7.99, 9.99, 0.99

toppings = ("basil", "extra cheese", "pepperoni", "garlic", "peppers", "tomatoes")
print("We'd like the " + toppings[1] + " and " + toppings[3] + " toppings.")

# Function calls
pizza_type('medium', 'thick')
pizza_type(crust = 'crispy thin', size = 'medium')
total_pizza_cost = calculate_cost(2, 4, medium_cost)

print("\nThe total cost is $" + str(total_pizza_cost) + ". Enjoy!")
```

A user-defined function is a code block (indicated by indented lines) that performs a specific task:
A **function definition** begins with the keyword def and a name. The parentheses after the function name can contain one or more **parameters**, which are variables that store information passed to the function. The parentheses are followed by a colon (:). The pizza_type() function has the parameters size and crust. It contains a print() function that prints a sentence with the size and crust values.

To execute (run) a function, you use a function call:
The **function call** consists of the function's name followed by parentheses that contain values for the parameters it has (if any). The function must be defined in the program before the function call. The pizza_type() function parameters, size and crust, receive values (called **arguments**) passed to the function in its function call. Just like the function's parameters, the arguments are separated by commas.

The first function call, pizza_type('medium', 'thick'), uses **positional arguments**, which are listed in the same order as the corresponding parameters in the function definition. This function call executes the pizza_type() function so it prints I would like a thick-crust, medium pizza. The second pizza_type() function call uses **keyword arguments**, which directly match the function's parameters to the argument values, so the order of arguments doesn't matter. This second function call executes the pizza_type() function so it prints I would like a crispy thin-crust, medium pizza.

A function can return a specified value, which is sent from the function to the function call line:
The calculate_cost() function calculates the total pizza cost. As you can see, arguments can be values or variables. The function returns the total_cost value with the return keyword. This return value is stored in the variable total_pizza_cost on the function call line. The total cost is $19.94. Enjoy! is then printed.

Hot Fresh Pizza

TOPPINGS
$0.99 each

Extra cheese

Garlic

Basil

Pepperoni

Peppers

Tomatoes

CRUST TYPES

Thick

Crispy Thin

PIZZA SIZE

Small $4.99

Medium $7.99

Large $9.99

```python
# Pizza lunch at the park program

table_occupancy = {
    'Chair #1': 'empty',
    'Chair #2': 'empty',
    'Chair #3': 'empty',
    'Chair #4': 'empty',
    }
# Loop through the dictionary's key:value pairs
for chair, status in table_occupancy.items():
    print(chair + " is " + status)

print("\nThis table is empty, let's eat here!\n")

# Loop through the dictionary's keys only
for chair in table_occupancy.keys():
    table_occupancy[chair] = 'taken'
    print(chair + " is now " + table_occupancy[chair])

print("\nThe pizza is delicious!")
```

To define a dictionary over multiple lines, it's good practice to format it like the `table_occupancy` dictionary. The optional comma after the last item makes it convenient to add another item if needed.

A `for` loop is used to loop through the key:value pairs of the `table_occupancy` dictionary:
`items()` is a built-in method that returns a list containing the key:value pairs in a dictionary. The first `for` loop in this program uses `items()` to loop through the items (key:value pairs) in the `table_occupancy` dictionary. Two variables (`chair` and `status` in this program) are used to store each key and value. Any name can be chosen for the variables that hold each key and value. For each iteration of the `for` loop, the variable `chair` stores the key of the current key:value pair and the variable `status` stores the value of the current key:value pair.

In the first iteration of the `for` loop, `chair` stores the value `'Chair #1'` and `status` stores the value `'empty'`. Chair #1 is empty is then printed. On the last iteration of the `for` loop, `chair` stores the value `'Chair #4'` and `status` stores the value `'empty'`. Chair #4 is empty is then printed.

Important note: In earlier versions of Python (below version 3.7), dictionaries were **unordered**, which meant that the order of a dictionary's key:value pairs was not preserved. The `items()` method returned the key:value pairs in an unpredictable order. Therefore, if you're using Python version 3.6 or below, you probably won't see each chair number printed in order. Dictionaries are **ordered** in Python version 3.7 and above.

To loop through only the keys of a dictionary, use the built-in method `keys()`:
The `keys()` method returns a list of the dictionary's keys. The next `for` loop uses the `keys()` method to loop through only the keys of the `table_occupancy` dictionary. The statement `table_occupancy[chair] = 'taken'` changes the value of `table_occupancy[chair]` from `'empty'` to `'taken'`. Therefore, during the first iteration of the `for` loop, Chair #1 is now taken is printed. After the `for` loop is completed, all of the dictionary's values have been changed from `'empty'` to `'taken'`.

```python
# Balloon program
# Function definitions
def choose_balloons(*our_choice):
    balloons = []     # create empty list
    for color_choice in our_choice:
        balloons.append(color_choice + ' balloon')
        print("I got a " + color_choice + ' balloon')
    return balloons # return list

def travel(transport, destination = 'our house'):
    print("\nWe are " + transport +  " to " + destination + ".")

balloon_colors = ['yellow', 'blue', 'purple', 'green', 'red', 'pink']
del balloon_colors[4] # delete 'red'
for balloon in balloon_colors:
    print("Available balloon color: " + balloon.title())

first_balloons = choose_balloons('blue', 'purple') # function call
second_balloons = first_balloons[:]
for balloon in second_balloons:
    print("I got another " + balloon)

del balloon_colors[1:3] # delete 'blue' and 'purple'
print("Balloon colors still available: " + str(balloon_colors))

travel('walking') # function call
```

The `choose_balloons()` **parameter** `*our_choice` **accepts an arbitrary number of arguments:**
The asterisk (∗) before `our_choice` makes it an empty tuple that accepts any number of arguments. `balloons` is assigned an empty list. In the `for` loop, each item in `our_choice` is concatenated with `' balloon'` and added to the `balloons` list, which is returned by the function.

The `del` **keyword deletes a list item without giving access to the value after it has been removed:**
Since the list index number starts at `0`, `del balloon_colors[4]` deletes the `'red'` item in the list.

A slice allows you to access part of a list with a starting and ending index:
`balloon_colors[1:3]` creates a slice containing items with indexes of `1` and `2` (`'blue'` and `'purple'`) because the ending index (`3`) isn't included. After this slice is deleted with `del`, the remaining balloon colors of `'yellow'`, `'green'`, and `'pink'` are printed. If you omit the starting index of a slice, it begins at the list's first item. If you omit the ending index, the slice ends through the last item. Therefore, the slice `[:]` includes the whole list. `first_balloons[:]` makes a copy of the `first_balloons` list. This copy is stored in `second_balloons`. `I got another blue balloon` and `I got another purple balloon` are printed.

In the `travel()` **function definition, the** `destination` **parameter has a default value:**
If you don't want to use the default value of `'our house'`, an argument can be specified in the function call. In a function definition, parameters with default values must be placed after all the parameters without default values. The argument `'walking'` matches up with the first parameter `transport`. The function prints `We are walking to our house.`

WE'RE SHOOTING HOOPS ON THE BASKETBALL COURT! IF THE BALL GOES
THROUGH THE HOOP, A POINT IS ADDED TO THE PLAYER'S SCORE. AFTER 15
THROWS, WE'LL COMPARE OUR SCORES TO SEE WHO GOT THE HIGHER SCORE (OR
IF THERE'S A TIE)!

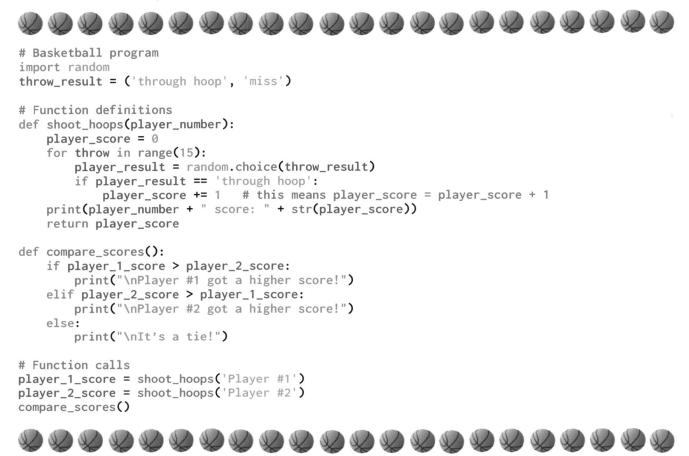

```
# Basketball program
import random
throw_result = ('through hoop', 'miss')

# Function definitions
def shoot_hoops(player_number):
    player_score = 0
    for throw in range(15):
        player_result = random.choice(throw_result)
        if player_result == 'through hoop':
            player_score += 1    # this means player_score = player_score + 1
    print(player_number + " score: " + str(player_score))
    return player_score

def compare_scores():
    if player_1_score > player_2_score:
        print("\nPlayer #1 got a higher score!")
    elif player_2_score > player_1_score:
        print("\nPlayer #2 got a higher score!")
    else:
        print("\nIt's a tie!")

# Function calls
player_1_score = shoot_hoops('Player #1')
player_2_score = shoot_hoops('Player #2')
compare_scores()
```

A module is a file that contains Python definitions (such as functions and variables) and statements:
A module allows you to organize related code in a separate file and easily use the code in different programs. random is
one of Python's built-in modules that is part of the **Python Standard Library**, which contains a collection of modules that
are useful for performing common tasks. random contains functions that generate random numbers or item selections.
The import keyword is used to import a module into your program so you can use its code. The statement import random
makes all the functions in the random module available to use in this program.

The choice() function in the random module returns a random item from a sequence:
To call a function from the module that was imported, place a dot (.) between the module name and function name.
random.choice(throw_result) passes the throw_result tuple to the choice() function. If choice() randomly returns
the 'through hoop' item from the throw_result tuple, the **addition assignment operator** (+=) adds a value of 1 to
player_score. The range() function starts at 0 by default if a start value isn't provided, so range(15) returns integers
0 through 14 (the stop value of 15 isn't included). After the for loop is completed (15 loops), the player's score is printed
and returned to the shoot_hoops() function call line. After the shoot_hoops() function is called for each player, the
returned player scores stored in player_1_score and player_2_score are compared in the compare_scores() function
to determine which score is higher or if there is a tie.

We're getting salad for dinner! One medium salad has lettuce, cheese, carrots, celery, and tomatoes in it and the other medium salad has lettuce, tomatoes, avocado, croutons, and walnuts in it.

```python
# Build a salad program
# Class definition
class Salad():
    """Modeling a salad."""

    def __init__(self, dressing, size):
        """Initialize attributes that describe the salad."""
        self.dressing = dressing   # assign dressing value to dressing attribute
        self.size = size   # assign size value to size attribute

    def salad_mix(self, *ingredients):
        """Add ingredients to the salad."""
        for ingredient in ingredients:
            print(ingredient + " added to the " + self.dressing + " salad.")

    def choose_bowl(self):
        """Choose the appropriate bowl for the salad size."""
        print(self.size + " bowl for the " + self.dressing + " salad\n")

# Create objects (instances) from the Salad class
salad_one = Salad('Ranch', 'Medium')
salad_two = Salad('Balsamic', 'Medium')

# Call methods on Salad class objects
salad_one.choose_bowl()
salad_two.choose_bowl()
salad_one.salad_mix('lettuce', 'cheese', 'carrots', 'celery', 'tomatoes')
salad_two.salad_mix('lettuce', 'tomatoes', 'avocado', 'croutons', 'walnuts')
```

A class allows you to create an object that models something in the real world:
A class contains a code block (indicated by indented lines), which provides a template (like a blueprint) for creating a specific **object**. **Attributes** are variables defined in the class. **Methods** are functions defined in the class. Class names are capitalized by convention. The class Salad models a salad with attributes of dressing and size and the methods salad_mix() and choose_bowl(). Each method has a **docstring**, which is a comment between three single (' ' ') or three double (" " ") quotation marks on each side. A docstring is often placed at the beginning of a function, module, or method to describe what it does. An object created from a class is called an **instance** of the class, as described below. Any number of instances can be created from a class. Every instance has its own attributes and methods.

In a class definition, every method's first parameter must be self, which refers to an instance:
In this program, salad_one = Salad('Ranch', 'Medium') creates a Salad instance called salad_one with attribute values of 'Ranch' and 'Medium'. A method call never includes an argument to the self parameter because Python automatically passes the instance itself as the first argument to the method. The special Python method __init__() (two underscores before and after init) runs automatically when an instance (object) is created. An instance attribute is accessed using a dot (.) after self, such as self.size. The __init__() method initializes attributes. The dressing attribute is assigned the value of the dressing parameter and the size attribute is assigned the value of the size parameter. The methods choose_bowl() and salad_mix() are called on the salad_one and salad_two instances. For the salad_one instance, choose_bowl() prints Medium bowl for the Ranch salad. For the salad_two instance, Medium bowl for the Balsamic salad is printed.

Limitless Salad Co.

Small - $5.00

Medium - $10.00

Large - $15.00

Walnuts   Chees   Tomatoes   Avocado

THE FOUR OF US ARE PLAYING MINIATURE GOLF! THERE ARE 18 HOLES IN THE GAME. EACH PLAYER IS ALLOWED 6 STROKES PER TURN TO GET THE GOLF BALL INTO THE CURRENT HOLE. EACH STROKE ADDS 1 POINT TO THE PLAYER'S SCORE. IF THE GOLF BALL MISSES THE HOLE AFTER 6 STROKES, THE PLAYER GETS A SCORE OF 7. THE PLAYER (OR PLAYERS IF THERE'S A TIE) WITH THE LOWEST TOTAL SCORE AT THE END WINS THE GAME.

```python
# Miniature golf program

from random import randint

# Each value of the dictionary is initialized as an empty list
scores = {'Player #1': [], 'Player #2': [], 'Player #3': [], 'Player #4': []}

# Add 18 randomly chosen numbers to each dictionary value (a list)
for hole_number in range(1,19):  # outer for loop
    print("Hole #" + str(hole_number) + " begins.")
    for player_number, score_list in scores.items():  # inner for loop
        golf_strokes = randint(1,7)   # get random integer from 1 through 7
        scores[player_number].append(golf_strokes)
        print(player_number + " scored " + str(golf_strokes))
    print("Hole #" + str(hole_number) + " is done.\n")

for player_number, score_list in scores.items():
    scores[player_number] = sum(score_list)
    print(player_number + " final score: " +  str(sum(score_list)))

winning_score = min(scores.values())

for player_number, score_list in scores.items():
    if score_list == winning_score:
        print("\n" + player_number + " won!")
```

A specific function can be imported from a module without importing the entire module:
from random import randint imports the randint() function from the random module, so randint() can be called by name in the program (without using the module name and dot). randint(1,7) generates a random integer that can be 1 through 7.

The outer for loop contains an inner (nested) for loop:
The outer for loop iterates through integers 1 through 18 with the range() function. During each outer for loop iteration, the inner for loop iterates through the four scores dictionary items. The random number from randint() is stored in golf_strokes, which is appended to the current iteration's dictionary value (a list). Once the outer for loop is completed, each value of the scores dictionary contains a list of 18 randomly chosen integers that represent the player's scores.

The built-in sum() function adds all 18 numbers from the current scores dictionary value:
The sum is stored in the scores dictionary value of the current for loop iteration. After the for loop, each dictionary value's list has been replaced by the sum of the list, which represents the player's total score. The values() method returns a list of all the values of a dictionary. The built-in min() function returns the dictionary's minimum value using the values() method on scores. The minimum value is stored in winning_score. The last for loop compares each value of the dictionary to winning_score to determine if the current player is a winner.

WE'RE EATING A LARGE CHOCOLATE CAKE FOR DESSERT! WE CHOSE THE TOPPINGS OF CHOCOLATE FROSTING, VANILLA CREAM, AND SPRINKLES. THE COST IS $20.00.

```python
# Cake for dessert program
class Dessert():
    """Modeling a dessert."""

    def __init__(self, size, cost):
        self.size = size
        self.cost = cost

    def about_dessert(self):
        print("\nThis " + self.size + " dessert is " + self.cost + ".")
class Cake(Dessert):
    """Modeling a dessert that is a cake."""

    def __init__(self, size, cost):
        super().__init__(size, cost)
        self.cake_type = "vanilla"

    def order_toppings(self, toppings):
        print("We would like these toppings on the cake:")
        for topping in toppings:
            print(topping.title())

our_cake = Cake('large', '$20.00')
our_cake.cake_type = "chocolate"
print("We're ordering a " + our_cake.cake_type + " cake.\n")

cake_toppings = ('chocolate frosting', 'vanilla cream', 'sprinkles')
our_cake.order_toppings(cake_toppings)
our_cake.about_dessert()
```

The Cake class is a child class of the Dessert parent class:
You can create a specialized class (called the **child class or subclass**) that inherits all the attributes and methods of another class (called the **parent class or superclass**). The parent class must be defined before the child class and the parent class name (Dessert) must be a parameter in the parentheses of the child class (Cake) definition. The __init__() method in Cake receives values for size and cost, which are 'large' and '$20.00' for the our_cake instance. A method in a child class with the same name as a method in its parent class overrides it. The Cake class needs its own __init__() method because its attribute cake_type is not in its parent class Dessert. Since the __init__() method in Cake overrides the __init__() method in its parent class Dessert, the special built-in function super() is used to call the __init__() method in the parent class Dessert. This allows a Cake instance (our_cake in this program) to initialize its size and cost attributes inherited from Dessert to values of 'large' and '$20.00'. The about_dessert() method, which our_cake inherits from Dessert, is called and prints This large dessert is $20.00.

A child class can define its own new attributes and methods:
In the Cake class definition, a new attribute cake_type is defined with a **default value** of "vanilla", so cake_type is not included as a parameter in parentheses. Outside of the Cake definition, the cake_type attribute is accessed with the instance name by our_cake.cake_type and the cake_type value is changed to "chocolate". The Cake class defines a new method specific to cakes called order_toppings(). The tuple stored in cake_toppings is passed to the order_toppings() method, which prints the toppings.

SINCE IT'S NOT RAINING, WE'RE WATCHING THE FIREWORKS SHOW. AFTER THE SHOW IS OVER IN **20** MINUTES, WE'LL GO BACK HOME.

```python
# Fireworks show program

# Function definition
def watch_fireworks():
    minutes = 0
    while True:
        minutes += 1
        if minutes < 15:
            continue     # go back to the beginning of the loop

        minutes_left = 20 - minutes

        if minutes < 19:
            print("Amazing grand finale! Minutes left: " + str(minutes_left))
        elif minutes == 19:
            print("One minute left!")
        elif minutes == 20:
            print("\nThat was a great fireworks show!\n")
            break     # exit the loop

sky = "not raining"

if sky != "raining":
    watch_fireworks()

print("Let's go home now!")
```

The majority of code is within the `watch_fireworks()` function, which doesn't contain any parameters or return a value. By including the code in a function, the main program code is more organized and easier to read, especially by using a descriptive function name. A function also allows a code block to be re-used and called multiple times in a program without the need to re-write it.

The not equal operator (!=) compares two values and returns `True` **if they are not equal:**
If the value on the left side of the **not equal operator (!=)** is equal to the value on the right side of the operator, the operator returns `False`. The expression `sky != "raining"` evaluates to `True` because `sky` holds the value `"not raining"`. The `if` statement is executed, which calls the `watch_fireworks()` function.

A while loop repeats if its condition is still true after the loop executes:
If the expression after `while` is true, its code block (indicated by indented lines) is executed. After it executes, the loop's code block is executed again if the `while` condition is still true. In this program, the `while` loop's condition is the Boolean value `True`, so the loop will run forever (this is an **infinite loop**) unless a `break` statement is reached, which immediately exits the loop. In the `while` loop's code block, `minutes` (which was initialized to `0`), is incremented by `1` during each iteration of the loop. In the first `if` statement, if the `minutes` value is less than `15` in the current loop, `continue` is executed. The `continue` statement causes the program to ignore the rest of the loop's code and return to the loop's first line (`while True:`). Once `minutes` becomes `15`, `minutes_left` is calculated and printed in the next `if` statement. Once `minutes` becomes `20`, the `break` statement causes the `while` loop to exit. The `watch_fireworks()` function has completed and `Let's go home now!` is printed.

WE MADE CHOCOLATE COOKIES AND WE'RE PLAYING A FUN VIDEO GAME.

🏆 🏆 🏆 🏆 🏆 🏆 🏆 🏆 🏆 🏆 🏆 🏆 🏆 🏆 🏆 🏆 🏆 🏆

```python
# Video game and cookies program

video_game = input("What video game should we play? ")
print("Ok, " + video_game.title() + " is a fun game.\n")

cookie_type = 'Chocolate Cookies'
if (cookie_type.lower() == 'chocolate cookies'):
    print("I love chocolate cookies!")

# Enter a numerical value (for example, 10 instead of "ten")
bake_timer = input("How many minutes does it take to bake cookies? ")
bake_timer = int(bake_timer)

waiting = True
while waiting:
    if bake_timer == 0:
        waiting = False
    else:
        print("Timer: " + str(bake_timer))
        bake_timer -= 1     # This means bake_timer = bake_timer - 1

print("\nLet's play " + video_game.title() + " now!")
```

🏆 🏆 🏆 🏆 🏆 🏆 🏆 🏆 🏆 🏆 🏆 🏆 🏆 🏆 🏆 🏆 🏆 🏆

The built-in function `input()` **reads text input from the user:**
`input()` works by printing the text within its parentheses (to prompt the user for text input) and pauses the program's execution to wait for the user to enter a line of text from an input device (a keyboard). After the user types a line of text and presses *Enter* on the keyboard, `input()` reads the text and returns it as a string. In this program, the string returned by the first `input()` function is stored in the variable `video_game`.

The equality operator (==) is case sensitive:
Two strings with the same values but different capitalization formats, such as `'Chocolate Cookies'` and `'chocolate cookies'`, are not considered equal by the equality (==) operator. To test if a string (stored in the program or entered by a user) equals a value that could have a different capitalization format, you can use the built-in string method `lower()`, which converts all of a string's letters into lowercase. `cookie_type.lower()` converts `'Chocolate Cookies'` into the `'chocolate cookies'` format, so the first `if` statement is true. String methods don't affect the original strings they act on, so the `cookie_type` variable still stores `'Chocolate Cookies'`.

A string can't be compared to a number and math cannot be performed with a string:
Since `input()` always returns a string, the string value of `bake_timer` needs to be converted into an integer so it can be used as a number. The built-in function `int()` converts the `bake_timer` string into an integer, which allows it to be compared to a number (0) and be decremented by 1 within the `while` loop.

variable `waiting` is initialized to `True` and used as the `while` loop test condition:
g is considered to be a **flag** variable, which is the concept of a variable's value being in one of two states (`True` or his program) that indicate a status (waiting or not waiting in this program). Within the `else` block, `bake_timer` d decremented by 1 with the **subtraction assignment operator** (-=). In the `if` statement, once the lue equals 0, `waiting` is set to `False` and the `while` loop is exited.

WE DID 15 ACTIVITIES TODAY AND WE'RE VERY HAPPY. TODAY WAS LIKE A FAIRY TALE...GOODNIGHT!

```python
# Goodnight program

from time import *
from datetime import date as current_date

# Function definition
def epic_test(activity_number, happy_value):
    if activity_number > 5 and happy_value == True:
        global epic_day
        epic_day = True

full_date = current_date.today()

number_of_activities = 15
very_happy = True
epic_day = None

print("In 5 seconds, it will be time for bed.")
sleep(5)

epic_test(number_of_activities, very_happy)

if epic_day:
    print("Today, " + str(full_date) + ", was like a fairy tale!")

print("Goodnight!")
```

All of a module's functions can be imported with the asterisk (*) operator after `import`:
`from time import *` copies all the functions in the `time` module into the program, so they can all be called by name. Be careful with this import approach because there will be a conflict if a function in the module has the same name as a function in your program. The `time` module contains the `sleep()` function, which suspends program execution for the number of seconds specified by the argument in parentheses. Once `sleep(5)` is executed, the `epic_test()` function call happens 5 seconds later.

A specific function or class can be imported and given a different name with the keyword `as`:
The `date` class is imported from the `datetime` module and the `date` class is renamed to `current_date`. The `today()` method in the `date` class returns the current local date (year, month, and day), so the current local date is stored in `full_date`.

The `global` **keyword is used to change the value of a global variable from within a function:**
A variable defined within a function is called a **local variable** and is only available to that function. A variable defined utside of a function is called a **global variable** and can be used anywhere in the program. Although a function can ss the global variable's value, it can't modify the value unless the variable is declared to be global with the `global` rd in the function. `epic_day` is a global variable that was initialized to `None`, which is an object in Python that has Since the `if` condition within `epic_test()` is true, the `global` keyword is used and `epic_day` is modified to be the function completes, the last `if` statement's condition is true and `full_date` is printed in a sentence before printed.

Run the programs!

Now you can share the story with YOUR computer! A Python interpreter is a program that executes the instructions from a Python program's source code (the code you wrote in your program). A Python IDE (integrated development environment) contains an editor in which you write code and a Python interpreter that executes the code. To write and run programs, you can download and install a Python IDE or use an online Python interpreter. There are many free online Python interpreters available, such as **OnlineGDB:** https://www.onlinegdb.com/online_python_interpreter

Type the program code into the editor and click the Run button to execute the program. In the console window at the bottom, you'll see the output from your program's print() function(s)!

Download Python

There are many IDEs you can use to write and run Python programs. IDLE is the IDE that is included with the download of Python from the official Python website's download page:

https://www.python.org/downloads/

1. Click the Download button at the top of the page to download the latest Python version for Windows.
2. Once the download finishes, click on it. If you're prompted to run the file, click Run.
3. In the next window, check the box for "Add Python [*version #*] to PATH". The box for Install launcher for all users (recommended) should be checked. Next, click "Install Now".
4. Once the installation is complete, open IDLE by clicking on IDLE within the Python folder in the start menu or searching for IDLE on the start menu's search bar and opening the app.

If you're using a Mac, click the link to download Python for Mac and click the latest release at the top of the page. Click on the Mac OS installer for your computer below the Files section at the bottom of the page. Click on the download once it is complete and follow the prompts to install Python.

Writing and running a Python script

When you first open IDLE, you'll see the Python IDLE shell, which can run one line of code at a time. You can type a line of code after the >>> prompt and press *Enter* on the keyboard to see the result printed from the interpreter. However, since you want to run multi-line programs (and be able to save your work!), follow these steps to create and run a Python script, which is a file that contains your Python program.

1. Click File -> New File, which opens a text editor window. Enter the program code.
3. Click File -> Save. Enter a filename (which has the extension .py). Click Save.
4. Click Run -> Run Module to run the script.
5. You'll see the output from your program's print() function(s) in the Python IDLE shell!

CONGRATULATIONS

You are now
a Python
programmer!

Code editors highlight different types of code with different colors, which is called syntax highlighting. For example, comments are all highlighted with the same color. This makes the code easier to read.

Have fun playing with the code and changing values (like ordering more pizzas!). If you get an error after running the code, fix the code and run it again! There are many common syntax errors. Make sure to:

- Include a colon (:) at the end of the line after def, class, for, while, if, else, or elif
- Indent all lines in a code block by the same number of spaces. You can't mix tabs and spaces.
- Insert the correct number of quotation marks and parentheses and place them correctly. You'll also get an error if you copy and paste quotes (such as from a word processor) written in unicode format ("Hi!") rather than ASCII format ("Hi!"). When you type quotation marks directly into the code editor, it will be in ASCII format.
- Write Python keywords with the correct spelling and capitalization. All keywords are lowercase except True, False, and None.

WHERE IS PYTHON USED?

Python is a popular high-level (human readable) programming language that can be used for a wide variety of applications. These notably include data science and analysis, artificial intelligence (AI) and machine learning, scientific and numeric computing, web development and apps, and game development. Python is also used in robotics for processing sensor data and controlling robots (such as the movement of robot arms) with high-level commands.

PHYSICAL COMPUTING WITH PYTHON

You can use Python in physical computing, which involves programming a computer to sense and interact with the outside world. For example, an external computer can control a robot or the computer can be embedded within the robot. Python is used to provide high-level instructions for reading sensor inputs (such as from a light or temperature sensor) and controlling outputs (such as a motor or LED).

A microcontroller has all the components of a computer contained in a single chip and is designed to be embedded within a larger device or appliance. The micro:bit (**https://microbit.org**) is a microcontroller development board designed for beginners that is commonly programmed in Python. The Raspberry Pi® (**https://www.raspberrypi.org**) is a single-board computer commonly programmed in Python. Unlike a microcontroller, the Raspberry Pi board is a higher power general-purpose computer that runs an operating system. It can be easily connected to the internet and used as a desktop computer by connecting it to a monitor, mouse, and keyboard. You can also connect electronic components to the Raspberry Pi to read sensor inputs and control outputs with Python code.

Raspberry Pi is a trademark of the Raspberry Pi Foundation

Notes

Notes

CPSIA information can be obtained
at www.ICGtesting.com
Printed in the USA
BVHW020833190721
612309BV00007B/880